Practice

Maths

Steve Mills and Hilary Koll

Contents

**Age 11–12
Year 7**
Key Stage 3

Introduction

Maths Practice

Practice Key Maths Skills is for anyone who is struggling to understand concepts in fractions and decimals and algebra. These topics can be difficult at first, but this simple, step-by-step approach should have you mastering tricky ideas in no time.

Pages 3–14 of this book are all about understanding fractions and decimals and equivalence. Pages 15–26 deal with proportion, improper fractions and mixed numbers, and it provides strategies for adding and subtracting fractions and ordering fractions and decimals. Also covered is using common denominators. Pages 27–38 of this book focus on algebra including simplifying expressions, expanding brackets, factorising and substituting.

How to use Maths Practice

Work through each section in order, reading all the clues and tips as you go through the exercises. You will need to cut out the cards in the book to use for some activities. Make sure you keep these cards in a safe place, such as an envelope, so you can re-use them.

When you feel confident with what is written on a particular page, turn over and try to answer the questions on the next page. Carefully mark all your answers to see how you got on. If you still have any difficulties and feel you need some more practice, try some of the activities again or re-read the tips and comments. If you feel confident and have got most of the questions right, move on to the next section.

You might find it helpful to make a list of all the key words that you come across in this book and write down the meanings. This will help you try to answer the questions.

This edition has been updated, 2014, to reflect National Curriculum changes.

Hachette UK's policy is to use papers that are natural, renewable and recyclable products and made from wood grown in sustainable forests. The logging and manufacturing processes are expected to conform to the environmental regulations of the country of origin.

Orders: please contact Bookpoint Ltd, 130 Milton Park, Abingdon, Oxon OX14 4SB. Telephone: (44) 01235 827720. Fax: (44) 01235 400454. Lines are open 9.00a.m.–5.00p.m., Monday to Saturday, with a 24-hour message answering service. Visit our website at www.hoddereducation.co.uk.

© Steve Mills and Hilary Koll 2013
Teacher's tip © Matt Koster 2013
First published in 2007 exclusively for WHSmith by
Hodder Education
An Hachette UK Company
Carmelite House, 50 Victoria Embankment,
London EC4Y 0DZ

This second edition first published in 2013 exclusively for WHSmith by Hodder Education.

Impression number   10 9 8 7 6
Year   2018

This edition has been updated, 2014, to reflect National Curriculum changes.

Cover illustration by Oxford Designers and Illustrators Ltd
All other illustrations by Fakenham Prepress Solutions, Fakenham, Norfolk NR21 8NN
Typeset in 16pt Folio by Fakenham Prepress Solutions, Fakenham, Norfolk NR21 8NN
Printed in Spain

A catalogue record for this title is available from the British Library.

ISBN: 978 1444 189 292

What are fractions?

Practice

Fractions describe *parts* of whole things.
- Fractions have one number on top of another.
  The number on the *bottom* is called the **denominator**.

These fractions are related:
They all have a denominator of 5.

- Fractions with a denominator of 5 are related because, for each of them, a whole thing has been split into **5 equal parts**.
  The whole thing could be anything such as:

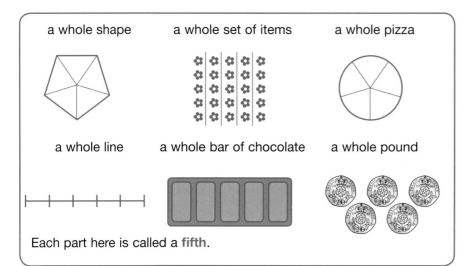

Each part here is called a **fifth**.

- The denominator shows how many equal parts the whole has been split into.
- The number on the *top* of a fraction is called the **numerator**.
  The numerator shows how many of the equal parts there are.

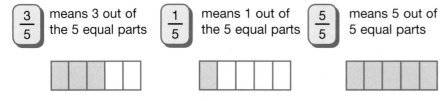

$\frac{3}{5}$ means 3 out of the 5 equal parts

$\frac{1}{5}$ means 1 out of the 5 equal parts

$\frac{5}{5}$ means 5 out of 5 equal parts

Try it

- Cut out the fraction cards on page 39.
- Practise describing what each fraction means.

Clues and tips

Here, the top number (the numerator) tells you how many equal parts to shade.

A common mistake

Some people think that the bottom number tells you how many parts are *not* shaded. But they are WRONG.

The bottom number (the denominator) tells you how many equal parts there are *altogether*.

This shows 2 out of 5, or $\frac{2}{5}$ (NOT $\frac{2}{3}$)

Starting with the denominator, count the total number of parts. Put that number on the bottom. Then count the shaded ones. Put that number on the top.

What next?

If you have managed to get these right, go on to page 5. If not, read the tips above again. You might find that the next page also helps you.

Try it yourself!

1. **Describe each fraction in words and shade each picture accordingly.**

$\frac{2}{3}$ 2 out of 3 equal parts $\frac{1}{6}$ _____

$\frac{7}{9}$ _____ $\frac{4}{5}$ _____

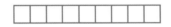

$\frac{3}{4}$ _____ $\frac{6}{6}$ _____

 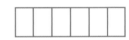

$\frac{5}{8}$ _____ $\frac{4}{7}$ _____

2. **What fraction of each of these circles is shaded?**

 —   —   —

 —   —   —

Teacher's tips

The parts of a whole can only be described as a fraction when **all** parts are **equal**: check this first. Remember that sometimes a shaded area of a shape may look unequal, but could be more than 1 part.

Fractions of amounts in your head

Practice

- Any whole thing (including numbers) can be split into fractional parts.
- Use the cut-out fraction cards on page 39.
- Find every fraction that has a **numerator** of 1, like these:

$$\frac{1}{6} \quad \frac{1}{2} \quad \frac{1}{5} \quad \frac{1}{8} \quad \frac{1}{4} \quad \frac{1}{3}$$

These fractions are called **unit fractions**.

- A unit fraction of any number can be found by dividing it by the **denominator** (bottom number), like this:

$$\frac{1}{6} \text{ of } 54 = 54 \div 6 = 9$$

Try these in your head:

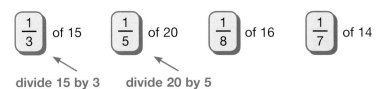

$$\frac{1}{3} \text{ of } 15 \qquad \frac{1}{5} \text{ of } 20 \qquad \frac{1}{8} \text{ of } 16 \qquad \frac{1}{7} \text{ of } 14$$

divide 15 by 3   **divide 20 by 5**

- Once you can find a unit fraction of a number, you can find *any* fraction of a number by multiplying, like this:

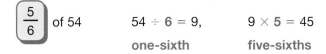

$$\frac{5}{6} \text{ of } 54 \qquad 54 \div 6 = 9, \qquad 9 \times 5 = 45$$

one-sixth   **five-sixths**

Try these in your head:

$$\frac{2}{3} \text{ of } 15 \qquad \frac{4}{5} \text{ of } 20 \qquad \frac{5}{8} \text{ of } 16 \qquad \frac{4}{7} \text{ of } 14$$

divide 15 by 3
to find one-third
then multiply by 2

- Remember: **Divide** by the denominator to find the unit fraction then
  multiply by the numerator.

Times tables

How good are you at your multiplication and division tables? It will help you a great deal if you know all your tables up to 12 × 12 – and it is never too late to learn.

Test yourself

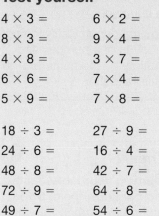

4 × 3 =	6 × 2 =
8 × 3 =	9 × 4 =
4 × 8 =	3 × 7 =
6 × 6 =	7 × 4 =
5 × 9 =	7 × 8 =
18 ÷ 3 =	27 ÷ 9 =
24 ÷ 6 =	16 ÷ 4 =
48 ÷ 8 =	42 ÷ 7 =
72 ÷ 9 =	64 ÷ 8 =
49 ÷ 7 =	54 ÷ 6 =

If you know these, then you probably know most of your tables. If there are some you do not know, LEARN them.

Take one fact a day and keep repeating it in different voices and accents. You will soon memorise them.

Clues and tips

Divide by the denominator to find a unit fraction of a number.

If you have trouble with your multiplication and division facts, write down the ones you get stuck on. Work out the answers on a calculator or using another method and write these down. Now learn a fact a day until you have learnt them all. It is not as hard as you think.

Divide by the denominator to find a unit fraction of a number, and then multiply by the numerator to find other fractions.

What next?

Keep learning your tables facts if you do not know them. If you understand how to find fractions of numbers, go on to page 7.

Try it yourself!

1. **Find the unit fractions of these numbers in your head.**

$\frac{1}{5}$ of 15 _____ $\frac{1}{8}$ of 16 _____ $\frac{1}{5}$ of 35 _____

$\frac{1}{6}$ of 24 _____ $\frac{1}{9}$ of 45 _____ $\frac{1}{7}$ of 21 _____

$\frac{1}{3}$ of 27 _____ $\frac{1}{7}$ of 42 _____ $\frac{1}{8}$ of 48 _____

$\frac{1}{4}$ of 28 _____ $\frac{1}{9}$ of 63 _____ $\frac{1}{8}$ of 64 _____

$\frac{1}{3}$ of 33 _____ $\frac{1}{6}$ of 36 _____ $\frac{1}{7}$ of 49 _____

2. **Find the fractions of these amounts in your head.**

$\frac{2}{5}$ of £15 _____ $\frac{3}{8}$ of 16 m _____ $\frac{4}{5}$ of 35 kg _____

$\frac{5}{6}$ of £24 _____ $\frac{4}{9}$ of 45 m _____ $\frac{3}{7}$ of 21 kg _____

$\frac{2}{3}$ of £27 _____ $\frac{2}{7}$ of 42 m _____ $\frac{5}{8}$ of 48 kg _____

$\frac{3}{4}$ of £28 _____ $\frac{8}{9}$ of 63 m _____ $\frac{3}{8}$ of 64 kg _____

$\frac{2}{3}$ of £33 _____ $\frac{5}{6}$ of 36 m _____ $\frac{6}{7}$ of 49 kg _____

Teacher's tips

Convert fractions into an equivalent fraction if it helps to make calculations easier. Using your times tables is always preferable, but if you forget use repeated addition of the denominator to find the unit fraction, then multiply by the numerator.

Fractions of amounts with a calculator

Practice

So far, fractions of numbers have been found mentally. Now a calculator will be used.

- When working out a fraction of an amount in our heads, the amount is **divided** by the **denominator** and **multiplied** by the **numerator**.

$\frac{5}{6}$ of £24 ← To answer this using a calculator, key in **24 ÷ 6 × 5** to get the answer 20.

- So it can be worked out with a calculator *exactly as it is in our heads*.
- Sometimes, however, teachers show a different way to find fractions of amounts on a calculator. It is actually the same method, but in a different order. Look at this:

> When three numbers are multiplied or divided together, it can be done in any order and the answer will be the same.
>
> **24 ÷ 6 × 5** gives the same answer as **5 ÷ 6 × 24**

Try it on a calculator.
- Teachers sometimes show this second way because it is in the order that the numbers appear in the question.

$\frac{5}{6}$ of £24   **5 ÷ 6 × 24**

Notice that the amount is still divided by the denominator.
- Learn to look at a fraction and think of it as a **division question**.

Try it

Pick a fraction card and write it as a division question.

$\boxed{\frac{4}{5}}$ = 4 ÷ 5

- So, to find a fraction of an amount on a calculator, just key in the fraction as a division question and then multiply by the amount.

$\frac{4}{5}$ of £30 = 4 ÷ 5 × 30

Two ways

This page shows two different ways of finding a fraction of an amount on a calculator.

It does not matter which way is chosen.

Whether it is done the same way as the mental method, or by thinking of the fraction as a division question and multiplying, the answer will be the same.

Word wise

The word 'of' in maths is usually shown by the multiplication sign.

$\frac{5}{6}$ of 24   is $\frac{5}{6}$ × 24

Remember to work from top to bottom: **numerator** divided by **denominator**.

Clues and tips

Remember to work from top to bottom: numerator divided by denominator.

Two ways

It does not matter which method you choose to answer question 2 (see page 7).

Decimal difficulties

Watch out for any answers which appear on the calculator that do not make sense. For example, how much is £24.4444444?

If you are talking about money, then round the answer to the nearest pence – £24.44.

What next?

If you are fine with this topic, go on to page 9.

If you find the second method on page 7 difficult, use the mental method on page 5.

Try it yourself!

1. **Write these fractions as division questions.**

$\frac{2}{5}$ _____ $\frac{3}{8}$ _____ $\frac{4}{5}$ _____

$\frac{5}{6}$ _____ $\frac{4}{9}$ _____ $\frac{3}{7}$ _____

2. **Find the fractions of these amounts on a calculator.**

$\frac{2}{5}$ of £75 _____ $\frac{3}{8}$ of 128 m _____ $\frac{4}{5}$ of 105 kg _____

$\frac{5}{6}$ of £72 _____ $\frac{4}{9}$ of 135 m _____ $\frac{3}{7}$ of 91 kg _____

$\frac{2}{3}$ of £69 _____ $\frac{2}{7}$ of 182 m _____ $\frac{5}{8}$ of 192 kg _____

3. **Find the fractions of these amounts on a calculator. Note that these answers may not be whole numbers.**

$\frac{2}{5}$ of £53 _____ $\frac{3}{8}$ of 60 m _____ $\frac{4}{5}$ of 49 kg _____

$\frac{5}{6}$ of £27 _____ $\frac{4}{9}$ of 55 m _____ $\frac{3}{7}$ of 72 kg _____

$\frac{2}{3}$ of £81 _____ $\frac{2}{7}$ of 34 m _____ $\frac{5}{8}$ of 102 kg _____

$\frac{3}{4}$ of £73 _____ $\frac{8}{9}$ of 75 m _____ $\frac{3}{8}$ of 95 kg _____

Teacher's tips

Press 'Clear' ('CE' on most calculators) before starting, and 'equals' (=) at the end, as some calculators keep a running total. Make a mental estimate and check the calculator's answer against this: always think whether the answer looks right.

Equivalence and simplest form

Practice

- Look at these two shapes. If both shapes were bars of chocolate, and you were given

  $\frac{4}{5}$ or $\frac{8}{10}$

  which would give you more chocolate? Neither. These fractions are **equivalent**.

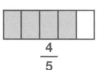
$\frac{4}{5}$

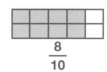
$\frac{8}{10}$

- Equivalent fractions have the same value but are made using different digits.

  $\frac{4}{5} = \frac{8}{10}$

  All of the fractions below are equivalent to one half.

$\frac{5}{10}$

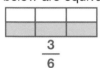
$\frac{3}{6}$

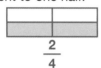
$\frac{2}{4}$

$\frac{4}{8}$

- To find fractions that are equivalent, the top *and* bottom numbers can be multiplied or divided by the same number.

$\div 5$

$\frac{5}{10} \quad \frac{1}{2}$

$\div 5$

$\times 3$

$\frac{1}{2} \quad \frac{3}{6}$

$\times 3$

$\div 2$

$\frac{2}{4} \quad \frac{1}{2}$

$\div 2$

$\times 4$

$\frac{1}{2} \quad \frac{4}{8}$

$\times 4$

These fractions are all equivalent to one half.

> As long as the top and bottom numbers are multiplied or divided by the same number, the new fraction will be equivalent.

Try it

Pick a fraction card and give at least three other equivalent fractions.

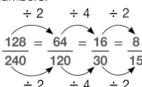
$\frac{4}{5}$ $\quad \frac{8}{10} \quad \frac{40}{50} \quad \frac{24}{30}$

- To change a fraction to its **simplest form**, divide until there is no other number (except 1) that divides exactly into the top *and* bottom numbers.

  $\div 2 \quad \div 4 \quad \div 2$

  $\frac{128}{240} = \frac{64}{120} = \frac{16}{30} = \frac{8}{15}$

  $\div 2 \quad \div 4 \quad \div 2$

  $\frac{128}{240}$ in its simplest form is $\frac{8}{15}$

  because there is no other number (except for 1) that divides into 8 and 15

Word wise

Equivalent means 'has the same value' or 'is worth the same'.

Equivalent fractions have the same value but are made using different digits.

To find equivalent fractions, multiply or divide the numerator *and* denominator by *any number you choose*. The resulting fraction will be equivalent.

Simplest form

When changing a fraction to its simplest form, always look to see what number will divide exactly into the numerator and into the denominator.

$\div 5$

$\frac{45}{100} \quad \frac{9}{20}$

$\div 5$

After dividing, check that there is not another whole number that will divide into both numbers. If there is not, the fraction is in its simplest form.

Clues and tips

An equivalent fraction can be made by multiplying or dividing the numerator *and* the denominator by the same number.

Simplest form

To change a fraction to its simplest form, *divide* the numerator and denominator by the same number. Keep doing this until there are no other numbers (except 1) that will divide into both numbers.

What next?

Make up more equivalent fractions using the fraction cards cut from page 39.

Practise your tables if you find it difficult to multiply and divide numbers in your head (see page 5).

Try it yourself!

1. **Write an equivalent fraction by multiplying or dividing as shown.**

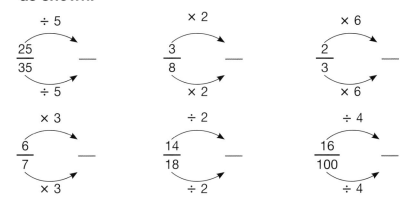

2. **Check to see which fractions are equivalent to $\frac{1}{4}$.**

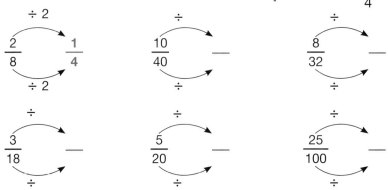

3. **Change these fractions to their simplest form.**

$\frac{24}{30}$ _____

$\frac{80}{100}$ _____

$\frac{36}{48}$ _____

$\frac{16}{68}$ _____

Teacher's tips

If a fraction has an even denominator **and** an even numerator, then it can always be simplified further (one way would be by halving both numerator and denominator). Remember this quick rule when simplifying fractions.

Denominators of 10, 100, etc. – decimals

Practice

Now you are going to learn how to convert fractions to **decimals**.

Decimals are like fractions. They are used to describe parts of whole things.

> The first step is to change the fraction to an **equivalent** one that has a **denominator** (bottom number) of 10 or 100, like these:
>
>
>
> Notice that each new fraction has a denominator of 10 or 100. Remember the new fraction is equivalent – it is worth the same.

- For a decimal, the columns after the decimal point stand for **tenths** and **hundredths**.

H T U . t h
3 2 0 . 2 7   So   0.2 means two-tenths $\frac{2}{10}$

     and   0.09 means nine-hundredths $\frac{9}{100}$

     and   0.37 means thirty-seven-hundredths $\frac{37}{100}$

- So, to convert a *fraction to a decimal,* it is first changed to an equivalent fraction with the denominator of 10 or 100.

  Then the digits of the **numerator** are written in the correct columns to make the decimal.

 So, three-fifths or six-tenths are both the decimal **0.6**

 So, seven-twentieths or thirty-five-hundredths are both the decimal 0.35

Try it

Do this for each of the fraction cards cut from page 39.

Why are decimals used?

Decimals are easier to use than fractions because they work like whole numbers.

With whole numbers:

Th H T U . t h th

ten units make one ten, ten tens make one hundred, ten hundreds make one thousand, and so on.

With decimals:

Th H T U . t h th

ten thousandths make one hundredth, ten hundredths make one tenth, ten tenths make one unit, and so on.

This makes it very easy to add, subtract, multiply and divide decimals.

Word wise

The decimal point is the dot separating the whole numbers from the part numbers.

Try it yourself!

1. **Write each of these fractions as a decimal.**

   $\frac{4}{10}$ __0.4__ $\frac{1}{10}$ _____ $\frac{6}{10}$ _____

   $\frac{8}{100}$ __0.08__ $\frac{2}{100}$ _____ $\frac{9}{100}$ _____

   $\frac{99}{100}$ __0.99__ $\frac{36}{100}$ _____ $\frac{61}{100}$ _____

2. **Convert each fraction into an equivalent one with a denominator of 10 or 100. Then write the fractions as decimals.**

   $\frac{3}{5} = \frac{6}{10} =$ __0.6__ $\frac{1}{2} = \frac{}{10} =$ _____

   $\frac{1}{50} = \frac{}{100} =$ _____ $\frac{3}{20} = \frac{}{100} =$ _____

   $\frac{21}{50} = \frac{}{100} =$ _____ $\frac{18}{20} = \frac{}{100} =$ _____

3. **Write these as fractions then change to their simplest form.**

   0.4 __$\frac{4}{10}$ or $\frac{2}{5}$__   0.6 _____   0.8 _____

   0.02 _____   0.05 _____   0.08 _____

   0.25 _____   0.75 _____   0.22 _____

Converting to decimals with a calculator

Practice

- Page 11 looked at fractions that can be easily converted to **equivalent** ones with a **denominator** of 10 or 100.

- However, NOT ALL fractions can be changed in this way.

  This fraction *cannot* be changed to an equivalent one with a denominator of 10 or 100.

- This fraction *can* be written as a **decimal**, but a calculator has to be used to find out what it is.
- Remember that a fraction can be thought of as a **division question**. So, just key the division question into a calculator and it will display the fraction as a decimal.

$$\frac{5}{17} = 5 \div 17 = \boxed{0.294117647}$$

The answer is then rounded so that it has 2 digits after the decimal point. It is said that the answer has been rounded to 2 **decimal places**.

So $\frac{5}{17}$ is the decimal 0.29 (to 2 decimal places).

- Some calculators have a key marked $\boxed{a^{b}\!/_{c}}$

This can help you to change between fractions and decimals.

Key in $\boxed{\frac{5}{9}}$ as $\boxed{5}$ $\boxed{a^{b}\!/_{c}}$ $\boxed{9}$ $\boxed{=}$ then keep pressing $\boxed{a^{b}\!/_{c}}$ to change between fractions and decimals.

Or key in a decimal followed by $\boxed{=}$ and then $\boxed{a^{b}\!/_{c}}$ to get the fraction in its **simplest form**.

Recurring decimals

Sometimes a decimal has a digit or digits that repeat, like 0.3333333333 or 0.272727272727.

These decimals are called recurring decimals.

Rounding

When a fraction cannot be expressed as an equivalent one with a **denominator** of 10 or 100 (or 1000 and so on), the decimal will probably have many digits after the decimal point.

Rather than writing all the digits, the number is rounded to 1 or 2 **decimal places** (so that the answer has 1 or 2 digits after the decimal point).

The words 'decimal places' can be shortened to **dp**.

Try it

Cut out the fraction cards on page 41.

Use a calculator to express each fraction as a decimal to 2 decimal places.

 $5 \div 9 =$
0.56 (to 2 dp)

Convert is another word for 'change'.

Rounding

When rounding, remember to look at the digit to the right of the last one needed in the answer. If it is 5 or more, the last digit of the answer should go up one.

If it is less than 5, the digit stays the same.

Less than 5
↓
0.294117647
0.29 to 2 dp

5 or greater
↓
0.37642577
0.38 to 2 dp

5 or greater
↓
0.59537868
0.60 to 2 dp

What next?

Do you feel that you understand the ideas in this book so far? Now is a good time to look back and re-read the pages to check that you still understand.

Try it yourself!

1. **Convert these fractions to decimals with a calculator. Write the answer shown on your calculator display.**

$\dfrac{1}{3}$ _____ $\dfrac{2}{3}$ _____

$\dfrac{4}{11}$ _____ $\dfrac{5}{13}$ _____

$\dfrac{4}{9}$ _____ $\dfrac{3}{7}$ _____

$\dfrac{2}{11}$ _____ $\dfrac{3}{13}$ _____

$\dfrac{4}{17}$ _____ $\dfrac{5}{15}$ _____

$\dfrac{4}{7}$ _____ $\dfrac{7}{9}$ _____

2. **Convert these fractions to decimals with a calculator. Round the answers to 2 decimal places.**

$\dfrac{3}{11}$ _____ $\dfrac{1}{9}$ _____

$\dfrac{1}{6}$ _____ $\dfrac{24}{29}$ _____

$\dfrac{7}{11}$ _____ $\dfrac{11}{13}$ _____

$\dfrac{21}{37}$ _____ $\dfrac{5}{9}$ _____

$\dfrac{12}{23}$ _____ $\dfrac{27}{29}$ _____

$\dfrac{15}{17}$ _____ $\dfrac{41}{99}$ _____

$\dfrac{12}{29}$ _____ $\dfrac{6}{17}$ _____

$\dfrac{9}{11}$ _____

Teacher's tips

Learn the decimal equivalent of common fractions and use this knowledge to estimate what the decimal for a fraction will be – check the answer on your calculator. It should be close to your estimate.

Proportion

Practice

- Now that you understand what fractions and decimals are, you can begin to solve **proportion** problems. The word 'proportion' means 'part of the whole', like this:

> A class has 24 girls and 8 boys. What proportion of the class is girls? (i.e. What part of the whole class is girls?)

This can be answered using a fraction, a decimal or a percentage.

There are 32 pupils in the class and 24 are girls,

so $\frac{24}{32}$ is the answer as a fraction.

This fraction can be given in its **simplest form**

$$\div 8$$
$$\frac{24}{32} \qquad \frac{3}{4}$$
$$\div 8$$

Three-quarters as a decimal is **0.75**.
Three-quarters as a percentage is **75%**.

Any of the answers $\frac{3}{4}$, 0.75 or 75% is acceptable.

- Try this one:

> A class has 16 girls and 14 boys. What proportion of the class is girls?

There are 30 pupils in the class and 16 are girls,

so $\frac{16}{30}$ is the answer as a fraction.

This fraction can be given in its simplest form

$$\div 2$$
$$\frac{16}{30} \qquad \frac{8}{15}$$
$$\div 2$$

Use a calculator to find this as a decimal.
8 ÷ 15 = 0.5333333333 or **0.53** to 2 dp.
As a percentage, 0.53 is **53%**.

- If you are given a proportion and asked to find 'how many …' you will need to **multiply** the proportion by the whole.

- Try this one:

> The proportion of girls in a class is $\frac{3}{4}$, 0.75 or 75%. There are 32 pupils in the class. How many are girls?

$$\frac{3}{4} \times 32 \qquad \text{or } 0.75 \times 32 \qquad \text{or } 75\% \times 32$$

Key any of these into the calculator to get the answer **24**.

- Remember:
  A fraction can be written as a division question: $\frac{3}{4}$ is **3 ÷ 4**

The % sign means 'out of 100' or 'divided by 100': **75%** is **75 ÷ 100**

Word wise

Proportion means 'part of the whole'. Proportions can be given as fractions, decimals or as percentages.

The percentage sign % means 'out of 100' or 'divided by 100'.

Remember that to change a fraction to its simplest form, the numerator *and* the denominator are divided by the same number. This is done until there is no number (except 1) that will divide into both numbers.

Clues and tips

At the bottom of page 13, the calculator key was introduced. This key helps to convert between fractions and decimals. It also helps to change a fraction to its simplest form.

Key in the fraction $\frac{16}{36}$ like this:

and when the equals button is pressed, the display shows the fraction $\frac{4}{9}$ like this:

This is $\frac{16}{36}$ in its simplest form.

What next?

Once you get a feel for fractions and decimals, solving problems becomes easier. However, if you are still finding these difficult, you might want to look back at pages 9 and 13.

If you struggle with percentages, you might find the *Practice Key Maths Skills Book 2* in this series useful.

If you find this sort of question okay, move on to page 17 to look at other types of fractions.

Try it yourself!

1. **What proportion of each of these classes is girls? Give each answer as a fraction in its simplest form.**

   A class has 16 girls and 20 boys:

   A class has:

   8 girls and 24 boys   12 girls and 20 boys

   15 girls and 25 boys   12 girls and 24 boys

2. **Solve these proportion problems, giving each answer as a fraction in its simplest form and as a decimal (to 2 decimal places).**

   In a box of chocolates 35 were milk, 18 were plain and 7 were white chocolate. What proportion of the chocolates was milk chocolate?

   _____

   In a box of chocolates 29 were milk, 27 were plain and 7 were white chocolate. What proportion of the chocolates was plain chocolate?

   _____

3. **Solve these questions.**

   The proportion of girls in a class is $\frac{5}{7}$. There are 35 pupils in the class. How many are girls?

   _____

   The proportion of girls in a class is $\frac{3}{8}$. There are 32 pupils in the class. How many are girls?

   _____

Teacher's tips

Proportion means 'part of the whole', so you must first calculate the **total**, or how many objects overall. When written as a fraction this is the denominator, and the numerator is the number in the set we are describing.

Practice

- Fractions are used to describe parts of a whole. But what happens when you want to describe some parts that make up *more than one whole*? Here, 5 quarters are shaded:

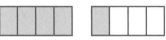

This can be written in two ways:

five-quarters $\dfrac{5}{4}$ or one whole and one quarter **1**$\dfrac{1}{4}$

The first way involves writing an **improper fraction**.

With an improper fraction, the number on top (the **numerator**) is *larger* than the number on the bottom (the **denominator**).

The second way involves writing a **mixed number**. A mixed number has a whole number *and* a fraction.

- It is important to be able to change from one form to the other.

Converting *from* improper fractions *to* mixed numbers

- Ask yourself:
  How many lots of the denominator are in the numerator? $\dfrac{13}{5}$
  How many 5s in 13?

- Work out the answer and write it with a remainder ... **2 r 3**
  The first number is the whole number.

  The remainder is the numerator of the fraction.   **2**$\dfrac{3}{5}$
  The denominator stays the same.

Converting *from* mixed numbers *to* improper fractions

- First do this multiplication:
  whole number × denominator   **2**$\dfrac{3}{5}$ **2 × 5 = 10**

  (This gives you how many fifths there are in the 2 whole ones.)

- Then add on the numerator (the extra fifths) ... **10 + 3 = 13**
  This is the new numerator of the improper fraction. $\dfrac{13}{5}$
  The denominator stays the same.

Try it

Write improper fractions to change to mixed numbers and vice versa.

Try it yourself!

1. Convert **these** improper fractions **to** mixed numbers.

$\dfrac{8}{3}$ _____ $\dfrac{14}{3}$ _____

$\dfrac{7}{5}$ _____ $\dfrac{19}{8}$ _____

$\dfrac{21}{9}$ _____ $\dfrac{9}{7}$ _____

$\dfrac{23}{4}$ _____ $\dfrac{14}{5}$ _____

$\dfrac{25}{6}$ _____ $\dfrac{9}{2}$ _____

$\dfrac{37}{7}$ _____ $\dfrac{34}{5}$ _____

$\dfrac{42}{5}$ _____ $\dfrac{50}{8}$ _____

$\dfrac{79}{9}$ _____

2. Convert **these** mixed numbers **to** improper fractions.

$3\frac{1}{4}$ _____ $5\frac{3}{4}$ _____

$4\frac{1}{5}$ _____ $4\frac{2}{3}$ _____

$2\frac{5}{8}$ _____ $3\frac{1}{6}$ _____

$6\frac{1}{2}$ _____ $8\frac{1}{3}$ _____

$5\frac{5}{6}$ _____ $7\frac{3}{4}$ _____

$6\frac{4}{5}$ _____ $2\frac{3}{8}$ _____

$4\frac{1}{7}$ _____ $3\frac{5}{9}$ _____

$5\frac{6}{7}$ _____

Teacher's tips

Remember: convert mixed numbers to improper fractions by multiplying the whole number by the denominator, then adding this to the numerator. Convert improper fractions by dividing the numerator by the denominator.

Practice

To add or subtract fractions, first make sure that the denominators of the fractions are the same. Then it is easy. Look at this:

$$\frac{3}{5} + \frac{1}{5} = \frac{4}{5}$$

Notice that the fractions being added have the same **denominators**.

The **numerators** are added. The denominator stays the same.

A common mistake

The most common mistake when adding fractions is to add the denominators too. The answer to

$$\frac{1}{4} + \frac{1}{4} =$$

... is not $\frac{2}{8}$

... it is $\frac{2}{4}$

Try it

Find two fraction cards with the same denominator.
Add them together.

$$\frac{4}{10} + \frac{9}{10} = \frac{13}{10} = 1\frac{3}{10}$$

If your answer is an improper fraction, change it to a mixed number.

Do this several times to get the hang of it.

Subtraction is the same. Just subtract the numerators.

- What do you do if the denominators are *not* the same?

$$\frac{2}{5} + \frac{3}{4} = \textbf{?}$$

- Do you remember how to change a fraction to an **equivalent** one? Remind yourself how by looking back at page 9. Change each fraction to an equivalent one so that they both have the *same* denominator.

To do this, look at both denominators. $\frac{2}{5}$ $\frac{3}{4}$

Q: What is the lowest number that both 4 and 5 divide exactly into?
A: 20

So, change both fractions to equivalent ones each with a denominator of 20:

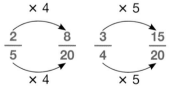

So, now the question is:

$$\frac{8}{20} + \frac{15}{20} = \frac{23}{20} = 1\frac{3}{20}$$

Denominator choosing

Sometimes it is not necessary to change both fractions to equivalent ones. Look at this question:

$$\frac{5}{6} + \frac{8}{12} =$$

Q: What is the lowest number that both 6 and 12 divide exactly into?
A: 12

Both fractions need to have the denominator 12, but one of them already has. Only the first fraction needs to change.

Clues and tips

If the denominators are the same, all you have to do is add the numerators (for addition) or subtract the numerators (for subtraction).

The denominator always stays the same.

Watch out

In question 2, there is quite a lot to think about when adding or subtracting fractions with different denominators. Start by deciding on the lowest number into which both denominators go. This will be the new denominator.

What next?

This section is quite difficult and you may be struggling with choosing an appropriate denominator, or with changing fractions to equivalent ones. Look back over page 9 to revise this. Knowing your tables will also help you with this (see page 5).

Try it yourself!

1. **Add or subtract these fractions. Notice that the denominators of each pair of fractions are the *same*. If your answer is an improper fraction, change it to a mixed number.**

$\frac{1}{5} + \frac{3}{5}$ _____ $\frac{2}{9} + \frac{4}{9}$ _____ $\frac{6}{7} + \frac{4}{7}$ _____

$\frac{6}{10} + \frac{7}{10}$ _____ $\frac{3}{8} + \frac{5}{8}$ _____ $\frac{3}{4} + \frac{3}{4}$ _____

$\frac{7}{11} - \frac{5}{11}$ _____ $\frac{5}{6} - \frac{1}{6}$ _____ $\frac{4}{5} - \frac{3}{5}$ _____

$\frac{11}{12} - \frac{3}{12}$ _____ $\frac{8}{9} - \frac{3}{9}$ _____ $\frac{9}{13} - \frac{5}{13}$ _____

2. **Add or subtract these fractions. Notice that the denominators of each pair of fractions are *NOT* the same.**

   You will need to change one or both of the fractions to equivalent ones so that the denominators of both fractions *are* the same.

$\frac{1}{5} + \frac{4}{10}$ _____ $\frac{6}{12} + \frac{4}{6}$ _____

$\frac{3}{5} + \frac{1}{2}$ _____ $\frac{3}{4} + \frac{3}{5}$ _____

$\frac{3}{4} - \frac{2}{3}$ _____ $\frac{2}{3} - \frac{1}{5}$ _____

$\frac{6}{7} - \frac{3}{14}$ _____ $\frac{5}{6} - \frac{2}{5}$ _____

Teacher's tips

If you can't think of a common denominator, one way that always works is to multiply the denominators by each other. Remember to multiply the numerator by the same amount as you multiply the denominator. You'll need to simplify the answer.

Practice

- Make sure that you know what each digit in a decimal stands for.
A **tenth 0.1** is the same as

$\frac{1}{10}$

and a **hundredth 0.01** is

$\frac{1}{100}$

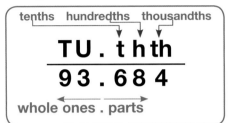

tenths hundredths thousandths

T U . t h th

9 3 . 6 8 4

whole ones . parts

Because tenths are larger than hundredths, it is easy to see that:

 0.4 is larger than **0.04**

- However, most people find this next bit difficult:
With **whole numbers**, the more digits a number has, the larger it is.

This is *not* necessarily true for decimals.

Look at this:

 0.4 is larger than **0.38**

- Because tenths are larger than hundredths, the tenths must be compared first. **0.4** has **4 tenths** and **0.38** only has **3 tenths** and some **hundredths**.
- When ordering decimals, begin by comparing the digit on the left and, if they are the same, move to the right to compare the next digit, etc.

0.6821   0.776   0.69   0.8   0.681

Which number has most tenths? ——————————➤ 0.<u>8</u>

Which has the next greatest number of tenths? ———➤ 0.7<u>7</u>6

Which numbers have the next greatest number of tenths?

0.<u>6</u>821   0.<u>6</u>9   0.<u>6</u>81

Which of these has most hundredths? ——————➤ 0.6<u>9</u>

Which numbers have the next greatest number of hundredths?

0.6<u>8</u>21   0.6<u>8</u>1

Which of these has most thousandths? ——————➤ 0.68<u>2</u>1

Which is the smallest number? ——————————➤ 0.681<u> </u>

So, the order, from largest to smallest, is:

0.8   0.776   0.69   0.6821   0.681

Know your decimals

Remind yourself about decimals by looking again at pages 11 and 12.

0.8 is larger than 0.75

Decimal difficulties

It is sometimes easier to see this if **0.4** is thought of as **0.40**.

If zeros are put on the end of the numbers with the fewest digits so they have the *same* number of digits, it is sometimes much easier to order them, like this:

0.8000
0.7760
0.6900
0.6821
0.6810

Put on extra zeros

Write zeros at the end of the decimal with the fewer digits so that both decimals have the same number of digits. This may help to decide which is larger.

Comparing fractions

For question 2, it might help to write out all the fractions on to small pieces of paper and to move them around to order them. Remember to start by comparing the tenths, and if the number of tenths is the same, compare the hundredths and so on.

What next?

You will need to be able to order decimals for the ideas on the next few pages. If you have been finding this difficult, make sure you write the zeros on the ends of the numbers so that all decimals have the same number of digits. This should help you with ordering. Otherwise, go on to page 23.

Try it yourself!

1. **Tick the larger decimal in each pair.**

0.40 ✓	0.38	0.8	0.753
0.82	0.81	0.45	0.54
0.82	0.823	0.6	0.603
0.9	0.88	0.751	0.7
0.151	0.21	0.31	0.3
0.3	0.295	0.863	0.86
0.274	0.2741	0.73	0.743

2. **Put each set of decimals in order of size from largest to smallest.**

0.134   0.413   0.314   0.14   0.3

largest _____ smallest

0.289   0.892   0.29   0.8   0.28

largest _____ smallest

0.525   0.252   0.52   0.25   0.5

largest _____ smallest

Teacher's tips

Ordering decimals is just the same as ordering whole numbers – try ignoring the decimal and thinking of it as a whole number, just remember to add zeros to each decimal first so they all have the same number of digits.

Ordering fractions

Practice

- Ordering fractions can be done in different ways. The first way is about just having a feel for what sizes fractions are.

  This fraction wall shows the relative sizes of different simple fractions.

  Use the fraction wall to compare and order this set of fractions.

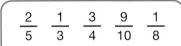

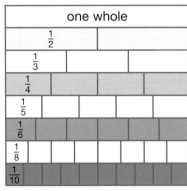

Fraction wall

Each strip of this fraction wall is worth one whole. The second strip shows two halves, the third strip shows three thirds, and so on.

To find the size of a fraction like three-fifths, look at the strip showing 5 equal parts. Count three across from the left to show the size of the fraction $\frac{3}{5}$

Write the fractions in order from smallest to largest.

smallest [   ] largest

- Sometimes there are too many fractions or the fractions are more difficult to order this way. So, another way is to use a calculator. First, key in each fraction as a **division question** to change each fraction to a decimal and then *order the decimals*.

  Remind yourself how to order decimals by looking again at page 21.

Fractions and calculators

Remember that a fraction can be keyed into a calculator as a division question.

Alternatively, some calculators have a $\boxed{a\%}$ key for converting between fractions and decimals (see page 13).

- Order these fractions by ordering the decimals from smallest to largest.

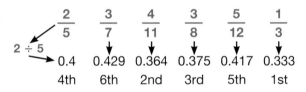

	$\frac{2}{5}$	$\frac{3}{7}$	$\frac{4}{11}$	$\frac{3}{8}$	$\frac{5}{12}$	$\frac{1}{3}$
$2 \div 5$ →	0.4	0.429	0.364	0.375	0.417	0.333
	4th	6th	2nd	3rd	5th	1st

smallest $\quad \frac{1}{3} \quad \frac{4}{11} \quad \frac{3}{8} \quad \frac{2}{5} \quad \frac{5}{12} \quad \frac{3}{7} \quad$ largest

Try it

Choose any five fraction cards. Convert them to decimals on a calculator and order them.

Do this several times to get the hang of it.

Fraction wall

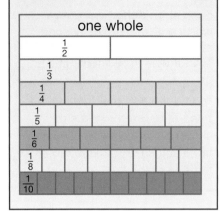

1. **Use the fraction wall to compare and order each set of fractions. Write the fractions in order from smallest to largest.**

$\frac{4}{5}$ $\frac{3}{4}$ $\frac{5}{6}$ $\frac{1}{8}$ $\frac{7}{8}$ $\frac{3}{5}$ $\frac{5}{10}$ $\frac{2}{3}$ $\frac{5}{8}$ $\frac{5}{6}$

_____   _____

$\frac{2}{3}$ $\frac{1}{4}$ $\frac{2}{5}$ $\frac{1}{8}$ $\frac{3}{10}$ $\frac{7}{10}$ $\frac{3}{4}$ $\frac{4}{6}$ $\frac{5}{8}$ $\frac{1}{2}$

_____   _____

What next?

Most people find using the fraction wall quite easy, but this is only useful if you have a fraction wall and are ordering simple fractions.

If you were still stuck at the end of page 22, you might be finding this second method difficult. Do not worry, the next page shows a third method for ordering fractions. Have a go and see if you prefer it.

It does not matter which method you use to order fractions.

2. **Using a calculator, convert each fraction to a decimal. Round any answers to 3 decimal places. Then order the fractions by ordering the decimals.**

$\frac{4}{5}$ $\frac{11}{14}$ $\frac{9}{10}$ $\frac{11}{13}$ $\frac{10}{12}$ $\frac{5}{7}$

↓   ↓   ↓   ↓   ↓   ↓

0.8 _____

smallest _____ largest

$\frac{2}{9}$ $\frac{3}{7}$ $\frac{4}{11}$ $\frac{1}{12}$ $\frac{6}{17}$ $\frac{2}{6}$

↓   ↓   ↓   ↓   ↓   ↓

_____

smallest _____ largest

Common denominators

Practice

- Do you remember that when adding and subtracting fractions, you had to change each fraction to an **equivalent** one so that both fractions had the *same* denominator? Look again at page 19.
  The *third way* of ordering fractions is to change all the fractions so that they have the *same* denominator. To do this, look at all the denominators and find the lowest number into which they will all divide.

$$\frac{4}{5} \quad \frac{5}{6} \quad \frac{7}{10} \quad \frac{11}{15} \quad \frac{2}{3}$$

They will all divide into the number 30.

Change all the fractions so that they have the denominator 30.
The new denominator that is chosen for all of the fractions is known as the **common denominator**.
Then the fractions are ordered from smallest to largest by looking at the **numerators**.

$$\frac{24}{30} \quad \frac{25}{30} \quad \frac{21}{30} \quad \frac{22}{30} \quad \frac{20}{30}$$

$$\text{4th} \quad \text{5th} \quad \text{2nd} \quad \text{3rd} \quad \text{1st}$$

Copy out the original fractions in that order for the answer.

smallest $\boxed{\dfrac{2}{3} \quad \dfrac{7}{10} \quad \dfrac{11}{15} \quad \dfrac{4}{5} \quad \dfrac{5}{6}}$ largest

Word wise

A common denominator is a denominator that two fractions share, such as $\frac{3}{5}$ and $\frac{4}{5}$. They share a common denominator of 5.

Here, a denominator is chosen that all the fractions can have in common.

Equivalent fractions

Remember how to change a fraction to an equivalent one?

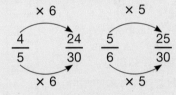

See page 9 to remind yourself how.

Try it

Choose three fraction cards. Look at the denominators. Find the lowest number into which they will all divide.

Convert the fractions to equivalent ones with this as the common denominator.

Now order them from smallest to largest by looking at the numerators.
Do this several times to get the hang of it.

Remember this

One way of finding a common denominator is to multiply all the numbers together, e.g.
$5 \times 3 \times 8 = 120$.

More confident with fractions and decimals?

Tick the following topics you feel confident with:

Understanding fractions (pages 3–4) ☐

Finding fractions of amounts in your head (pages 5–6) ☐

Finding fractions of amounts on a calculator (pages 7–8) ☐

Equivalence and simplest form (pages 9–10) ☐

Understanding decimals (pages 11–12) ☐

Converting to decimals with a calculator (pages 13–14) ☐

Proportion (pages 15–16) ☐

Mixed numbers and improper fractions (pages 17–18) ☐

Adding and subtracting fractions (pages 19–20) ☐

Ordering decimals (pages 21–22) ☐

Ordering fractions (pages 23–24) ☐

Read through any pages again to make sure you understand.

Try it yourself!

1. **Convert each of these fractions to equivalent ones so that they all have the common denominator shown.**

$$\frac{7}{9} \qquad \frac{3}{4} \qquad \frac{5}{6} \qquad \frac{11}{12} \qquad \frac{2}{3}$$

$$\frac{}{36} \qquad \frac{}{36} \qquad \frac{}{36} \qquad \frac{}{36} \qquad \frac{}{36}$$

2. **Convert each of these fractions to equivalent ones with a common denominator. Use this information to list the fractions in order of size from smallest to largest.**

$$\frac{3}{5} \qquad \frac{13}{20} \qquad \frac{5}{8}$$

smallest _____ largest

$$\frac{3}{8} \qquad \frac{2}{3} \qquad \frac{1}{12} \qquad \frac{2}{6}$$

smallest _____ largest

$$\frac{4}{5} \qquad \frac{7}{9} \qquad \frac{13}{15} \qquad \frac{2}{3}$$

smallest _____ largest

Teacher's tips

It's easy to make mistakes when converting several fractions to equivalents or decimals, so always make clear notes showing your working that you can then go back and check. Writing the equivalents underneath the original fraction is ideal.

Simplifying expressions

In algebra, letters are used to stand for numbers.

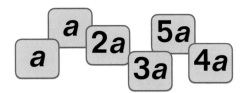

- Cut out the 'a' cards on page 43.
- Turn them face down and pick *three* of them.
- Write them like this:

  $a + 2a + a$ _____

  $a + 2a + a$ is called an **expression**.

- Now find out how many a's there are altogether.

  $a + 2a + a = 4a$ _____ = _____

  (4a means '4 lots of a')

- This process is called **simplifying**.
  (Writing the expression in a simpler, shorter way.)

Try it

Pick three cards and simplify the expression.

$$a + 2a + 3a = 6a$$

Do this several times to get the hang of it.
Then try picking more than three cards.
- Remember this word:
  simplifying – writing an expression more simply

Clues and tips

An expression can be written in many different ways and still be worth the same, such as:

> $a + a + a$

or $a + 2a$

or $2a + a$

or $3a$

or $3 \times a$

or $a \times 3$

Which expressions in question 1 are equivalent (worth the same)?

Watch out

It is easy to forget to write the letter a in the answer.

The letter doesn't matter

Treat question 3 in the same way as question 1.

It does not matter what the letter is.

What next?

If you are fine with this topic, go on to page 29.

If not, practise more with your 'a' cards.

Try it yourself!

1. **Simplify these.**

$a + 3a + a =$ ___5a___ $a + a + a + a + 2a =$ _____

$a + a + 2a + a =$ _____ $3a + a + 2a + a + a =$ _____

$2a + 3a + 2a =$ _____ $3a + a + a + a + 5a =$ _____

$a + 5a + 5a + a =$ _____ $6a + 4a + 2a + a + 2a =$ _____

2. **True or false? Have these expressions been correctly simplified?**

$a + a + a = 3a$ ___true___ $a + 3a + a + 3a = 8a$ _____

$7a + a + 3a = 11a$ _____ $5a + a + 3a + a = 9a$ _____

$3a + 3a = 9a$ _____ $6a + 3a + a + 4a = 14$ ___false___

$a + 5a + a = 7a$ _____ $4a + 4a + 2a + a + 2a = 13a$ _____

$a + 6a + 2a = 9$ _____ $10a + 10a + 5a + 5a = 25a$ _____

3. **Simplify these – notice that different letters are used.**

$m + 3m + m =$ ___5m___ $g + g + 2g + g + 3g =$ _____

$p + p + 2p + 3p =$ _____ $3s + s + s + s + s =$ _____

$2c + 3c + 4c =$ _____ $9d + d + d + d + 4d =$ _____

$y + 5y + 5y + 2y =$ _____ $7k + 3k + 2k + k + 2k =$ _____

Teacher's tips

You will have used 'p' when calculating money. Algebra is the same, except rather than standing for 'pence' the letter stands for a number. Remember in algebra the letter chosen isn't important because it's not signifying a unit.

Collecting like terms

Practice

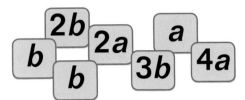

- Now cut out the 'b' cards on page 43.
- Shuffle them with the 'a' cards.
- Pick four cards. (Hopefully, some will be 'a' cards and some will be 'b' cards.)

- Write them out like this:

  a + 2*b* + *b* + 4*a*

- To **simplify** these expressions, find out *how many a's* there are and then *how many b's* there are and write this down.

  $a + 2b + b + 4a = 5a + 3b$ (Notice that the *a*'s do not mix with the *b*'s.)

  Now try simplifying your expression!

- This process is called **collecting like terms**.

Why is algebra needed?

Algebra is used in all sorts of situations, such as helping companies to make more profit, helping engineers build roads and bridges, or even helping doctors to decide how much of a drug to give a person.

In each of these situations, there are usually one or more unknown values that need to be calculated from a number of known values.

Try it

Pick four cards and simplify the **expression** by collecting like terms.

$$b + 2a + 4b + a = 3a + 5b$$

Do this several times to get the hang of it.

Then try picking more than four cards.

- Remember this:

  collecting like terms – grouping letters that are the same

Watch out

3*a* + 5*b* could also be written as 5*b* + 3*a*. They are both the same. It does not matter in which order you put the letters.

Clues and tips

The reason different letters are used in an expression is that they could stand for different numbers.

Here are some number cards showing the numbers 2 and 5.

a is written on the back of the number 2 cards and *b* is written on the back of the number 5 cards. So 3*a* + 4*b* is made using 3 cards with 2 on and 4 cards with 5 on, giving a total of 26.

More than two letters

It does not matter how many letters there are – just do not mix them.

It can help to cross letters off as they are counted.

What next?

If you are fine with this topic, go on to page 31.

If not, practise more with your 'a' and 'b' cards.

Try it yourself!

1. **Simplify these by collecting like terms.**

   $a + 3a + 2b + 4b = $ __4a + 6b__ $a + b + a + b + 2a = $ _____

   $a + b + 2b + a = $ _____ $3b + b + 2b + a + a = $ _____

   $2a + 3b + 2a = $ _____ $6a + b + b + b + 2a = $ _____

2. **Which of these expressions, when simplified, has the answer 4*a* + 3*b*? Tick them.**

   $a + 3a + 2b + b = $ __4a + 3b__ ✓ $a + 2b + a + b + 2a = $ _____

   $a + b + 3a + 2a = $ _____ $3a + b + 2b + a = $ _____

   $4a + b + 2b = $ _____ $a + a + 3b + a + a = $ _____

3. **Collect like terms – notice that different letters are used.**

   $g + 3g + h + h = $ __4g + 2h__ $m + m + 2n + n + 3m = $ _____

   $2c + 3d + c + 4c = $ _____ $9e + f + f + f + 4e = $ _____

   $x + 5y + 5x + 2y = $ _____ $7j + 3k + 2j + k + 2k = $ _____

4. **Collect like terms – with *more than two* different letters.**

   $a + 3a + b + c + 2b + 3c + a + 4a = $ __9a + 3b + 4c__

   $2p + 5q + q + r + 2r + p + p + 3q = $ _____

   $x + 4x + 2y + 3z + 2y + 5z + 6x + 4y = $ _____

Teacher's tips

Because the letters in algebra stand for numbers, they cannot be mixed up. 2a + 3b cannot be added up to be 5a, 5b or 5ab. Try giving each of the letters a (different) value and solving 2a + 3b and you'll see why.

Adding and subtracting letters

Practice

So far, letters have just been added together. They can be subtracted, too.

- Use all the cut-out 'a' cards.
- Place the 5a card face up on the table.
- Turn the others face down.
- Pick a card and *subtract* that amount from 5a.
- Write it like shown below and work out the answer. Do this twice.

$5a - a = 4a$ $5a -$ _____ $5a -$ _____

This is still **simplifying** an **expression**.

- Now also use the cut-out 'b' cards.
- Place the 5b card next to the 5a card.
- Write this as 5a + 5b.
- Turn the rest face down and mix them with the others.
- Pick a card and *subtract* that amount from 5a + 5b.
- Write it like this and remember to keep the letters separate:

$5a + 5b - a = 4a + 5b$
$5a + 5b - \underline{\quad} = \underline{\quad\quad}$

Only subtract *a* from 5a, the 5b stays the same.

Fancy a take-away?

Letters can only be subtracted from things of the same type, for example 5a subtract 4b can only be written as $5a - 4b$. This is because *a*'s and *b*'s are not the same.

5a subtract 4a can be written more simply because they are both *a*'s. It can be written as just *a*.

Try it

Pick a card and subtract it from 5a + 5b.

$$\boxed{5a} + \boxed{5b} - \boxed{4a} = a + 5b$$

Do this several times to get the hang of it.

Try picking two cards to subtract.

- Answers sometimes contain negatives, like this:

$5a + 5b - 4a - 3a = -2a + 5b$
$5a + 5b - 4b - 2b = 5a + {-}b$ or $5a - b$

Watch out

Looking at just the *a*'s, it can be seen that $5a - 4a - 3a$ gives $-2a$ (negative 2a). The 5b stays the same.

If an add sign and a negative sign appear next to each other, this is written as a subtraction sign.

Clues and tips

It is important to look very carefully to see whether each part is added or subtracted to avoid getting the completely wrong answer.

Do not forget that $1b$ is written as just b.

Take it one step at a time

When simplifying the expressions in question 2, take the letter *a* first and go through each part of the expression. It can help to *cross letters off* or *underline* them as they are counted. Then move on to the letter b.

Negative issues

Do not panic if there are a negative number of *a*'s or *b*'s. Just write the negative sign in the answer.

What next?

If you are fine with this topic, go on to page 33. If you find the negative ones difficult, draw a number line from -10 to 10 to help you.

Try it yourself!

1. **Simplify these.**

   $5a - a =$ _____ **4a** $6a - 2a =$ _____

   $8a - a - a =$ _____ $5a + 5b - 2a =$ **3a + 5b**

   $5a + 5b - a - 2a =$ _____ $5a + 5b - a - b =$ _____

   $5a + 5b - 4b =$ _____ $7a + 4b - 4a - 3a =$ _____

   $3a + 10b - 4b =$ _____ $7a + 3b - 2b - a =$ _____

   $5a + 2b - b - 4a =$ _____ $8a + 4b - 4b - a - a =$ _____

2. **These are even harder to simplify. Can you do it?**

   $10a + 10b - 4a - a - b - a - a - 2b =$ **3a + 7b**

   $10a + 10b - 2a - 2a - 3b - a - b - b =$ _____

   $12a + 8b - 2a - 5a - 4b - a - b - a =$ _____

   $7a + 11b - 2b - 5b - 4b - a - 2a - a =$ _____

3. **Simplify these – the answers might be negative.**

   $2a + 4b - 6b =$ **2a – 2b**

   $4a + 2b - 8b =$ _____

   $2a + 3b - 3a =$ **–a + 3b**

   $3a + 6b - 6a =$ _____

   $2a + 4b - 3a - b =$ _____

   $4a + 3b - 8b - 3a =$ _____

Teacher's tips

It often helps in algebra to give the letters meanings in your head – 'a' for apples, 'b' for bananas for instance – and to then visualise the problem. Just remember to use the letters when writing the algebra!

Constants and variables

Practice

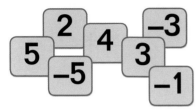

Where did the word 'algebra' come from?

An Arabic mathematician called al-Khwarizmi first used the word 'algebra' over 1000 years ago.

- Now cut out the number cards on page 45. Any number on its own (not one next to a letter) is called a **constant**. This is because a number, unlike letters, is always *constant*; it stays the same. Constants can be positive or negative.

- Letters in **expressions** are known as **variables**. This is because, in an expression, the value of a letter can *vary*. For example, in the expression **2y**, *y* could stand for 3, 7, −10 or any number.

- Shuffle the constant cards with the variable cards ('*a*' and '*b*' cards).

- Pick five cards. (Hopefully, some will be variables and some will be constants.)

- Write them out like this, adding them all together:

  $a + 2b + b + 4 + {}^-1$ If an add sign and a negative sign appear next to each other, they are written as a subtraction sign.

  $a + 2b + b + 4 - 1$

- To **simplify** these expressions, find out *how many a's* there are and *how many b's* there are, and then add the constants together.

  $a + 2b + b + 4 - 1 = a + 3b + 3$

  Now try with your expression.

  _____

Don't mix them

Notice that the *a*'s do not mix with the *b*'s and that the **variables** are kept separate from the constants.

Again, it does not matter in which order the parts are given so, $a + 3b + 3$ could be written as $3 + a + 3b$, etc. Generally, however, most people put variables first and constants at the end.

Try it

Pick several cards, add them together and simplify the expression by **collecting like terms**.

$$b + 2a + 4b + {}^-2 = 2a + 5b - 2$$

How many cards can you simplify?

Try it yourself!

1. **Simplify these by collecting like terms.**

   $4a + 5b + 2a + 2b + 3b + 6 + 4 + - 3 =$ ___$6a + 10b + 7$___

   Think of this part as $6 + 4 - 3$

   $2a + 6b + 2a + 5a + 4b + b + 5 + -2 =$ _____

   $7a + 4b + 2b + 5 + 2a + 3 + 2a + -10 =$ _____

   $4a + b + 5b + -4 + 3a + 5 + 2b + 2 =$ _____

   $10 + 2a + 5 + -5 + 3b + 5a + b + -1 =$ _____

2. **Try simplifying these expressions, but notice that some of the parts are *subtracted* rather than *added*.**

   $7a + 4b - 2a + 5b - 2b + 9 + 1 - 4 =$ _____

   $3a + 5b - 3b - 2a + 5b + 4 - 5 + 2 =$ _____

   $6a + 3b + 5a - 4a - 3b + 6 + 1 - 10 =$ _____

   $- 2a + 4b + 5a - 2b + 8 - 3 - 9 =$ _____

3. **Simplify these – notice that different letters are used.**

   $3c + 5d - 3c - 2d + 2c + 6 - 5 + 3 =$ _____

   $6m + 3n + 5m + 6 - 4n - 3m + 1 - 4 =$ _____

   $- 2g + 3h + 5g + 10 - 2h - 3 - 7 =$ _____

   $3s - t + 4 + 5s - 6 + 2 + 11t - 7s =$ _____

Substitution

Practice

- Now you are going to learn how to **substitute**.
- You will need just your 'a' cards again. Turn them face down.

Imagine you are about to win lots of money.

If you pick this card you win an amount of money.

If you pick this card you win twice the amount.

If you pick this card you win three times the amount and so on.

- Pick one of your 'a' cards.
  How much money would you win?
  Until someone tells you what 'a' is worth you do not know!
  How much would you win if a is worth £5?
  What if a is worth £10?
  Or if a = £1000?
- This is called **substituting**.
  Like footballers who get substituted (put in place of another player), here a **number** is put in place of a **letter**.

- Find these two cards:

- Substitute the following values for a and b to find how much money you would win:

  If a = £5 and b = £2   3 lots of £5 + 4 lots of £2 = £15 + £8 = £23

  If a = £3 and b = £5   _____

  If a = £10 and b = £6   _____

  If a = £6 and b = £1   _____

Word wise

To substitute means 'to exchange one thing for another'. In sport, players are substituted. When solving problems in algebra, numbers are substituted for letters.

One of the most useful parts of algebra for everyday life is being able to substitute a number into an expression or formula.

Remember this

Do not forget that 3a means '3 lots of a' or '3 × a'.

When substituting a value for a into the expression 3a, it must be multiplied by 3, like this:

If a = 5, then 3a = 15.

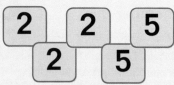
Try it yourself!

1. **Substitute the number given for the letter in these expressions.**

   If $a = 4$, find the value of $5a$ <u>$5a = 20$</u>

   If $y = 2$, find the value of $7y$ _____

   If $d = 5$, find the value of $8d$ _____

   If $k = 11$, find the value of $6k + 1$ <u>$6k + 1 = 67$</u>

   If $x = 10$, find the value of $9x + 5$ _____

   If $g = 3$, find the value of $5g + 4$ _____

   If $q = 1$, find the value of $10q - 2$ _____

2. **Substitute the numbers for the letters to find the value of each expression.**

   If $a = 4$ and $b = 2$, find the value of $5a + 3b$ <u>$20 + 6 = 26$</u>

   If $a = 2$ and $b = 5$, find the value of $3a + 2b$ _____

   If $a = 9$ and $b = 1$, find the value of $a + 4b$ _____

   If $a = 3$ and $b = 6$, find the value of $2a + 2b$ _____

3. **If $x = 6$ and $y = 9$, find the values of each expression.**

   $x + 5y - 1$ _____ $3x + 2y + 5$ _____

   $2x + 2y - 5$ _____ $5x - y + 3$ _____

   $3x + 10y - 8$ _____ $7x - 3y + 14$ _____

   $6x + 7y - 11$ _____ $-2x + 4y - 6$ _____

Teacher's tips

It can be helpful to rewrite algebraic expressions using brackets when substituting. If $a=2$ and $b=3$, then $5a + 10b$ could be written as $(5\times2) + (10\times3)$. This makes it easier to keep track of substitutions and check calculations.

Expanding brackets and factorising

Practice

- Here are some expressions:

$a + b$ $c + 3$ $2d - 5$ $6e - f + 2$

- Look what happens when each expression is **multiplied** by a **constant**.

$4(a + b)$ $5(c + 3)$ $2(2d - 5)$ $3(6e - f + 2)$

Notice that they all have **brackets**. Brackets show that what is outside the bracket is multiplied by everything inside.

- Expressions *with* brackets can also be written *without* brackets. To do so, multiply the number outside the bracket by **each part** inside.

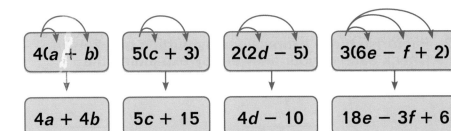

$4(a + b)$ $5(c + 3)$ $2(2d - 5)$ $3(6e - f + 2)$

$4a + 4b$ $5c + 15$ $4d - 10$ $18e - 3f + 6$

This is called **expanding the brackets**. It is a type of simplifying.

The opposite of expanding is called **factorising**. Factorising means finding a **factor** that divides into each part of an expression.

$18e - 3f + 6$ ——**Factorising**——→ $3(6e - f + 2)$

3 is a factor of **each part**

- Remember:

  expanding – multiplying what is outside the brackets by each part inside. (**Getting rid of the brackets.**)

  factorising – finding a factor that divides into each part and putting it outside brackets. (**Putting back the brackets.**)

Remember this

A number on its own (not next to a letter) is called a **constant**. It can be positive or negative.

Multiplying by variables

A simple expression can also be multiplied by a **variable**, like the letter x or y, to create an expression such as $x(x + 2)$.

Draw arrows

When expanding brackets, it helps to draw arrows to remind you to multiply the part outside by *every part* inside.

Factorising facts

A **factor** is a number or a variable that divides exactly into another number.

When **factorising**, take this factor outside and put brackets around the rest of the expression.

Teacher's tips

This type of algebra takes lots of concentration and it helps to write notes when solving these problems. Ideally when expanding or factorising, write each new element of the expression underneath the original so you can easily check them.

Clues and tips

The most common mistake in expanding brackets is to forget to multiply what is outside the brackets by *every part* inside.

When expanding

$5(a + b)$

the answer is NOT

$5a + b$

the answer is

$5a + 5b$

Example

Look at this example for multiplying several letters by a number:

If multiplying $3a$ by 5, remember that $3a$ means '3 lots of a'.

Multiplying that by 5, gives 15 lots of a which is $15a$.

What next?

Do you feel that you understand the ideas in the book so far? Now is a good time to look back and go over the pages to check that you still understand.

More confident in algebra now?

Tick the following topics you feel confident with:

Simplifying expressions (pages 27–28) ☐

Collecting like terms (pages 29–30) ☐

Adding and subtracting letters (pages 31–32) ☐

Constants and variables (pages 33–34) ☐

Substitution (pages 35–36) ☐

Expanding brackets and factorising (pages 37–38) ☐

Try it yourself!

1. **Simplify these expressions by expanding the brackets.**

$2(a + b) = $ ___$2a + 2b$___ $4(y - 2) = $ ___$4y - 8$___

$5(c + 2) = $ _____ $3(k + 6) = $ _____

$6(m + n) = $ _____ $7(2a - 1) = $ _____

$4(5g + h) = $ _____ $6(2f - e) = $ _____

$8(10s + 3t) = $ _____ $5(3y - 7) = $ _____

$3(a + 3b - 2) = $ _____ $2(m + 7n + 4) = $ _____

$5(4c + d - 3e) = $ _____ $6(g - 2h - 5) = $ _____

2. **Factorise these expressions by putting brackets in. Check each of your answers by expanding the brackets.**

$2a + 2b = $ ___$2(a+b)$___ $2c - 4 = $ ___$2(c-2)$___

$5d + 10 = $ _____ $3k + 6 = $ _____

$6m + 4n = $ _____ $2a - 12 = $ _____

$10g + 20h = $ _____ $6f - 2e = $ _____

$15s + 3t = $ _____ $5y - 25 = $ _____

$2a + 4b - 6 = $ ___$2(a + 2b - 3)$___ $2m + 6n + 4 = $ _____

$15c + 5d - 10e = $ _____ $8g - 4h - 12 = $ _____

First set of fraction cards

$\frac{1}{25}$	$\frac{7}{10}$	$\frac{3}{4}$	$\frac{1}{2}$
$\frac{4}{25}$	$\frac{9}{10}$	$\frac{2}{5}$	$\frac{1}{5}$
$\frac{1}{50}$	$\frac{3}{20}$	$\frac{3}{10}$	$\frac{1}{4}$
$\frac{13}{50}$	$\frac{11}{20}$	$\frac{3}{5}$	$\frac{1}{10}$
$\frac{49}{50}$	$\frac{19}{20}$	$\frac{4}{5}$	$\frac{1}{20}$

Activity cards

Activity cards

Second set of fraction cards

$\frac{2}{9}$	$\frac{8}{9}$	$\frac{2}{7}$	$\frac{5}{17}$
$\frac{11}{17}$	$\frac{1}{3}$	$\frac{6}{7}$	$\frac{4}{9}$
$\frac{23}{24}$	$\frac{1}{6}$	$\frac{3}{13}$	$\frac{1}{9}$
$\frac{17}{19}$	$\frac{2}{3}$	$\frac{5}{19}$	$\frac{3}{11}$
$\frac{4}{99}$	$\frac{5}{6}$	$\frac{4}{7}$	$\frac{5}{11}$

Activity cards

'b' cards

'a' cards

3b	b	3a	a
4b	b	4a	a
4b	2b	4a	2a
5b	2b	5a	2a
5b	3b	5a	3a

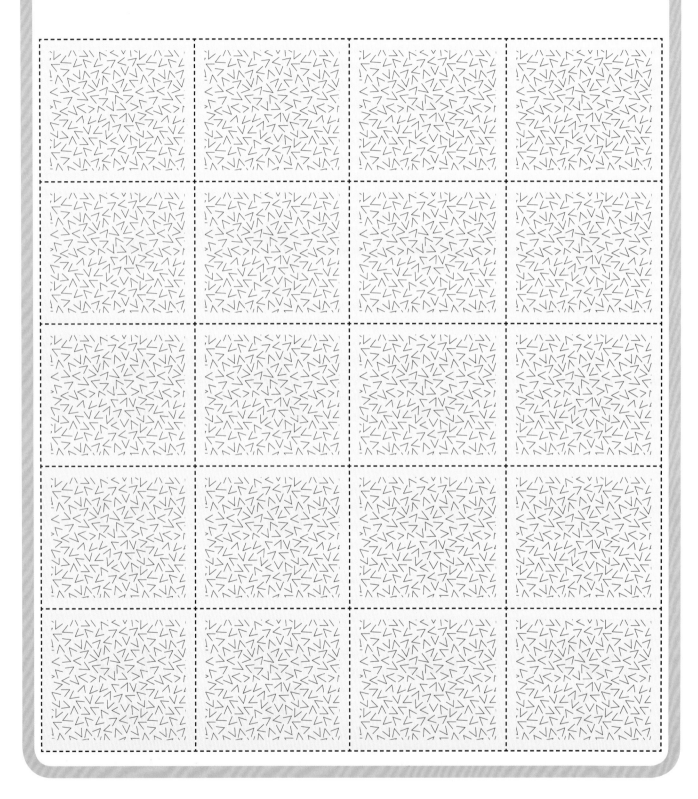

Activity cards

Addition, subtraction and equals signs

Constant cards

+	1	-1	1
+	1	-2	2
+	1	-3	3
+	1	-4	4
=	=	-5	5

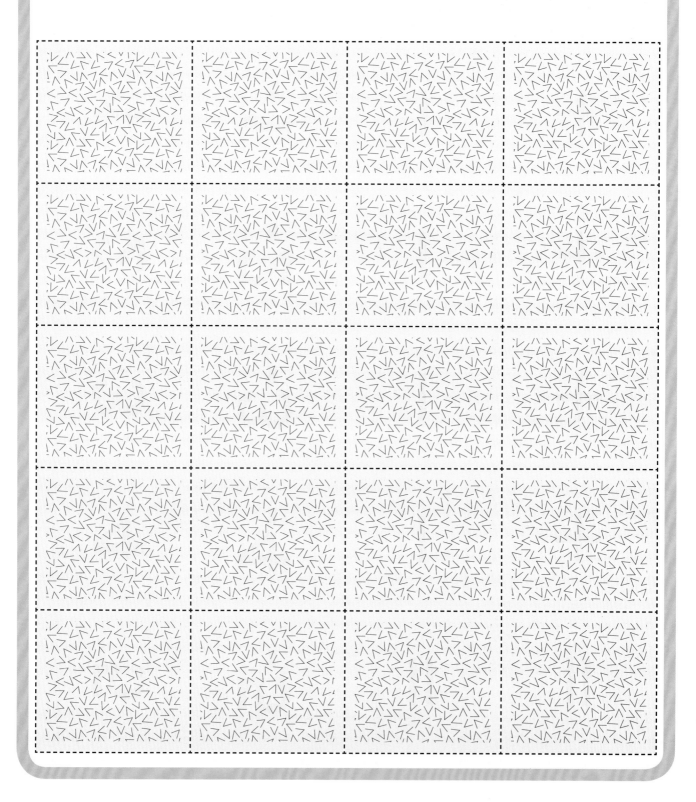

Answers

WHAT ARE FRACTIONS? (PAGE 4)
1. 2 out of 3 equal parts   1 out of 6 equal parts
    7 out of 9 equal parts   4 out of 5 equal parts
    3 out of 4 equal parts   6 out of 6 equal parts
    5 out of 8 equal parts   4 out of 7 equal parts

2. $\dfrac{1}{8}$ $\dfrac{2}{3}$ $\dfrac{1}{6}$ $\dfrac{4}{10}$ $\dfrac{5}{12}$ $\dfrac{7}{10}$

FRACTIONS OF AMOUNTS IN YOUR HEAD (PAGE 6)
1. 3   2   7   4   5   3   9   6   6   7   7   8   11   6   7
2. £6   6 m   28 kg   £20   20 m   9 kg   £18   12 m   30 kg   £21   56 m   24 kg   £22   30 m   42 kg

FRACTIONS OF AMOUNTS WITH A CALCULATOR (PAGE 8)
1. $2 \div 5$ $3 \div 8$ $4 \div 5$ $5 \div 6$ $4 \div 9$ $3 \div 7$
2. £30   48 m   84 kg   £60   60 m   39 kg   £46   52 m   120 kg
3. £21.20   22.5 m   39.2 kg   £22.50   24.44 m   30.86 kg   £54   9.71 m   63.75 kg   £54.75   66.67 m   35.63 kg

EQUIVALENCE AND SIMPLEST FORM (PAGE 10)
1. $\dfrac{5}{7}$ $\dfrac{6}{16}$ $\dfrac{12}{18}$ $\dfrac{18}{21}$ $\dfrac{7}{9}$ $\dfrac{4}{25}$

2. $\dfrac{1}{4}$ $\dfrac{1}{4}$ $\dfrac{1}{4}$ $\dfrac{1}{6}$ $\dfrac{1}{4}$ $\dfrac{1}{4}$

3. $\dfrac{4}{5}$ $\dfrac{4}{5}$ $\dfrac{3}{4}$ $\dfrac{4}{17}$

DENOMINATORS OF 10, 100, ETC. – DECIMALS (PAGE 12)
1. 0.4   0.1   0.6   0.08   0.02   0.09   0.99   0.36   0.61

2. $\dfrac{6}{10} = 0.6$ $\dfrac{5}{10} = 0.5$ $\dfrac{2}{100} = 0.02$ $\dfrac{15}{100} = 0.15$ $\dfrac{42}{100} = 0.42$ $\dfrac{90}{100} = 0.9$

3. $\dfrac{4}{10}$ or $\dfrac{2}{5}$ $\dfrac{6}{10}$ or $\dfrac{3}{5}$ $\dfrac{8}{10}$ or $\dfrac{4}{5}$ $\dfrac{2}{100}$ or $\dfrac{1}{50}$ $\dfrac{5}{100}$ or $\dfrac{1}{20}$ $\dfrac{8}{100}$ or $\dfrac{2}{25}$

   $\dfrac{25}{100}$ or $\dfrac{1}{4}$ $\dfrac{75}{100}$ or $\dfrac{3}{4}$ $\dfrac{22}{100}$ or $\dfrac{11}{50}$

CONVERTING TO DECIMALS WITH A CALCULATOR (PAGE 14)
1. 0.3333333   0.6666666   0.3636363   0.3846153   0.4444444   0.4285714
    0.1818181   0.2307692   0.2352941   0.3333333   0.5714285   0.7777777
2. 0.27   0.11   0.17   0.83   0.64   0.85   0.57   0.56   0.52   0.93   0.88   0.41   0.41   0.35   0.82

PROPORTION (PAGE 16)
1. $\dfrac{4}{9}$ $\dfrac{1}{4}$ $\dfrac{3}{8}$ $\dfrac{3}{8}$ $\dfrac{1}{3}$

2. $\dfrac{7}{12}$ or 0.58 $\dfrac{3}{7}$ or 0.43

3. 25   12

MIXED NUMBERS AND IMPROPER FRACTIONS (PAGE 18)
1. $2\dfrac{2}{3}$ $4\dfrac{2}{3}$ $1\dfrac{2}{5}$ $2\dfrac{3}{8}$ $2\dfrac{3}{9}$ or $2\dfrac{1}{3}$ $1\dfrac{2}{7}$ $5\dfrac{3}{4}$ $2\dfrac{4}{5}$ $4\dfrac{1}{6}$ $4\dfrac{1}{2}$

   $5\dfrac{2}{7}$ $6\dfrac{4}{5}$ $8\dfrac{2}{5}$ $6\dfrac{2}{8}$ or $6\dfrac{1}{4}$ $8\dfrac{7}{9}$

2. $\dfrac{13}{4}$ $\dfrac{23}{4}$ $\dfrac{21}{5}$ $\dfrac{14}{3}$ $\dfrac{21}{8}$ $\dfrac{19}{6}$ $\dfrac{13}{2}$ $\dfrac{25}{3}$ $\dfrac{35}{6}$ $\dfrac{31}{4}$ $\dfrac{34}{5}$ $\dfrac{19}{8}$ $\dfrac{29}{7}$ $\dfrac{32}{9}$ $\dfrac{41}{7}$

ADDING AND SUBTRACTING FRACTIONS (PAGE 20)
1. $\dfrac{4}{5}$ $\dfrac{6}{9}$ or $\dfrac{2}{3}$ $\dfrac{10}{7}$ or $1\dfrac{3}{7}$ $\dfrac{13}{10}$ or $1\dfrac{3}{10}$ $\dfrac{8}{8}$ or 1 $\dfrac{6}{4}$ or $1\dfrac{2}{4}$ or $1\dfrac{1}{2}$

   $\dfrac{2}{11}$ $\dfrac{4}{6}$ or $\dfrac{2}{3}$ $\dfrac{1}{5}$ $\dfrac{8}{12}$ or $\dfrac{2}{3}$ $\dfrac{5}{9}$ $\dfrac{4}{13}$

2. $\dfrac{6}{10}$ or $\dfrac{3}{5}$ $\dfrac{14}{12}$ or $1\dfrac{2}{12}$ or $1\dfrac{1}{6}$ $\dfrac{11}{10}$ or $1\dfrac{1}{10}$ $\dfrac{27}{20}$ or $1\dfrac{7}{20}$ $\dfrac{1}{12}$ $\dfrac{7}{15}$ $\dfrac{9}{14}$ $\dfrac{13}{30}$

ORDERING DECIMALS (PAGE 22)
1. 0.40   0.8   0.82   0.54   0.823   0.603   0.9   0.751   0.21   0.31   0.3   0.863   0.2741   0.743
2. 0.413   0.314   0.3   0.14   0.134   0.892   0.8   0.29   0.289   0.28   0.525   0.52   0.5   0.252   0.25

Answers

ORDERING FRACTIONS (PAGE 23)

$\dfrac{1}{8}$ $\dfrac{1}{3}$ $\dfrac{2}{5}$ $\dfrac{3}{4}$ $\dfrac{9}{10}$

ORDERING FRACTIONS (PAGE 24)

1. $\dfrac{1}{8}$ $\dfrac{3}{4}$ $\dfrac{4}{5}$ $\dfrac{5}{6}$ $\dfrac{7}{8}$ $\dfrac{5}{10}$ $\dfrac{3}{5}$ $\dfrac{5}{8}$ $\dfrac{2}{3}$ $\dfrac{5}{6}$ $\dfrac{1}{8}$ $\dfrac{1}{4}$ $\dfrac{3}{10}$ $\dfrac{2}{5}$ $\dfrac{2}{3}$ $\dfrac{1}{2}$ $\dfrac{5}{8}$ $\dfrac{4}{6}$ $\dfrac{7}{10}$ $\dfrac{3}{4}$

2. 0.8   0.786   0.9   0.846   0.833   0.714

$\dfrac{5}{7}$ $\dfrac{11}{14}$ $\dfrac{4}{5}$ $\dfrac{10}{12}$ $\dfrac{11}{13}$ $\dfrac{9}{10}$

0.222   0.429   0.364   0.083   0.353   0.333

$\dfrac{1}{12}$ $\dfrac{2}{9}$ $\dfrac{2}{6}$ $\dfrac{6}{17}$ $\dfrac{4}{11}$ $\dfrac{3}{7}$

COMMON DENOMINATORS (PAGE 26)

1. $\dfrac{28}{36}$ $\dfrac{27}{36}$ $\dfrac{30}{36}$ $\dfrac{33}{36}$ $\dfrac{24}{36}$

2. $\dfrac{3}{5} = \dfrac{24}{40}$ $\dfrac{5}{8} = \dfrac{25}{40}$ $\dfrac{13}{20} = \dfrac{26}{40}$

$\dfrac{1}{12} = \dfrac{2}{24}$ $\dfrac{2}{6} = \dfrac{8}{24}$ $\dfrac{3}{8} = \dfrac{9}{24}$ $\dfrac{2}{3} = \dfrac{16}{24}$

$\dfrac{2}{3} = \dfrac{30}{45}$ $\dfrac{7}{9} = \dfrac{35}{45}$ $\dfrac{4}{5} = \dfrac{36}{45}$ $\dfrac{13}{15} = \dfrac{39}{45}$

SIMPLIFYING EXPRESSIONS (PAGE 28)

1. $5a$ $6a$ $5a$ $8a$ $7a$ $11a$ $12a$ $15a$

2. true true true false false false true true false false

3. $5m$ $8g$ $7p$ $7s$ $9c$ $16d$ $13y$ $15k$

COLLECTING LIKE TERMS (PAGE 30)

1. $4a + 6b$ (or $6b + 4a$) $4a + 2b$ (or $2b + 4a$)
$2a + 3b$ (or $3b + 2a$) $2a + 6b$ (or $6b + 2a$)
$4a + 3b$ (or $3b + 4a$) $8a + 3b$ (or $3b + 8a$)

2. $4a + 3b$ ✓ $4a + 3b$ ✓
$6a + b$ $4a + 3b$ ✓
$4a + 3b$ ✓ $4a + 3b$ ✓

3. $4g + 2h$ (or $2h + 4g$) $5m + 3n$ (or $3n + 5m$)
$7c + 3d$ (or $3d + 7c$) $13e + 3f$ (or $3f + 13e$)
$6x + 7y$ (or $7y + 6x$) $9j + 6k$ (or $6k + 9j$)

4. $9a + 3b + 4c$ (or these in any order)
$4p + 9q + 3r$ (or these in any order)
$11x + 8y + 8z$ (or these in any order)

ADDING AND SUBTRACTING LETTERS (PAGE 32)

1. $4a$ $4a$
$6a$ $3a + 5b$ (or $5b + 3a$)
$2a + 5b$ (or $5b + 2a$) $4a + 4b$ (or $4b + 4a$)
$5a + b$ (or $b + 5a$) $4b$
$3a + 6b$ (or $6b + 3a$) $6a + b$ (or $b + 6a$)
$a + b$ (or $b + a$) $6a$

2. $3a + 7b$ (or $7b + 3a$)
$5a + 5b$ (or $5b + 5a$)
$3a + 3b$ (or $3b + 3a$)
$3a$

3. $2a - 2b$ (or $-2b + 2a$)
$4a - 6b$ (or $-6b + 4a$)
$-a + 3b$ (or $3b - a$)
$-3a + 6b$ (or $6b - 3a$)
$-a + 3b$ (or $3b - a$)
$a - 5b$ (or $-5b + a$)

CONSTANTS AND VARIABLES (PAGE 34)

1. $6a + 10b + 7$ (or these in any order)
$9a + 11b + 3$ (or these in any order)
$11a + 6b - 2$ (or these in any order)
$7a + 8b + 3$ (or these in any order)
$7a + 4b + 9$ (or these in any order)

2. $5a + 7b + 6$ (or these in any order)
$a + 7b + 1$ (or these in any order)
$7a - 3$ (or these in any order)
$3a + 2b - 4$ (or these in any order)

3. $2c + 3d + 4$ (or these in any order)
$8m - n + 3$ (or these in any order)
$3g + h$ (or these in any order)
$s + 10t$ (or these in any order)

SUBSTITUTION (PAGE 35)

£23   £29   £54   £22

SUBSTITUTION (PAGE 36)

1. $5a = 20$ $7y = 14$ $8d = 40$ $6k + 1 = 67$
$9x + 5 = 95$ $5g + 4 = 19$ $10q - 2 = 8$

2. 26   16   13   18

3. 50   41   25   24   100   29   88   18

EXPANDING BRACKETS AND FACTORISING (PAGE 38)

1. $2a + 2b$ $4y - 8$
$5c + 10$ $3k + 18$
$6m + 6n$ $14a - 7$
$20g + 4h$ $12f - 6e$
$80s + 24t$ $15y - 35$
$3a + 9b - 6$ $2m + 14n + 8$
$20c + 5d - 15e$ $6g - 12h - 30$

2. $2(a + b)$ $2(c - 2)$
$5(d + 2)$ $3(k + 2)$
$2(3m + 2n)$ $2(a - 6)$
$10(g + 2h)$ $2(3f - e)$
$3(5s + t)$ $5(y - 5)$
$2(a + 2b - 3)$ $2(m + 3n + 2)$
$5(3c + d - 2e)$ $4(2g - h - 3)$